THE MAHABHARATA
CHILDREN'S ILLUSTRATED CLASSICS

DRAUPADI *the* FIRE CHILD

Retold by CHARU AGARWAL DHANDIA
Art KAVITA SINGH KALE   *Design* RACHITA RAKYAN

RUPA

Published by
Rupa Publications India Pvt. Ltd 2020
7/16, Ansari Road, Daryaganj
New Delhi 110002

Sales centres:
Allahabad Bengaluru Chennai
Hyderabad Jaipur Kathmandu
Kolkata Mumbai

Edition copyright © Rupa Publications Pvt. Ltd 2020

All rights reserved.
No part of this publication may be reproduced, transmitted,
or stored in a retrieval system, in any form or by any means, electronic, mechanical, photocopying,
recording or otherwise,
without the prior permission of the publisher.

ISBN: 978-81-291-4973-2

First impression 2020

10 9 8 7 6 5 4 3 2 1

The moral right of the author has been asserted.

Printed at Nutech Print Services - India

This book is sold subject to the condition that it shall not, by way of trade or otherwise, be lent,
resold, hired out, or otherwise circulated, without the publisher's prior consent, in any form of
binding or cover other than that in which it is published.

Charu Agarwal Dhandia weaves together her two biggest passions—studying Indian classical literature and creative storytelling. She is an economist by training and works in the social development space.

Kavita Singh Kale's background as an artist and a designer enables her to draw a thin line between design following functionality and pure self-expression. This has helped her evolve as a transmedia artist. Her work includes art installations, children's books, comics, paintings and videos.

Rachita Rakyan combines over 15 years of expertise in graphic design and art direction with deep understanding of functionality and aesthetics across print, publishing, branding and digital media.

CONTENTS

KURU DYNASTY — IV-V
KEY CHARACTERS — VI-VII
PANDAVAS IN EKACHARYA — 1
THE BIRTH OF DRAUPADI — 5
THE SPINNING FISH — 19
THE CONTEST — 31
THE UNUSUAL WEDDING — 43

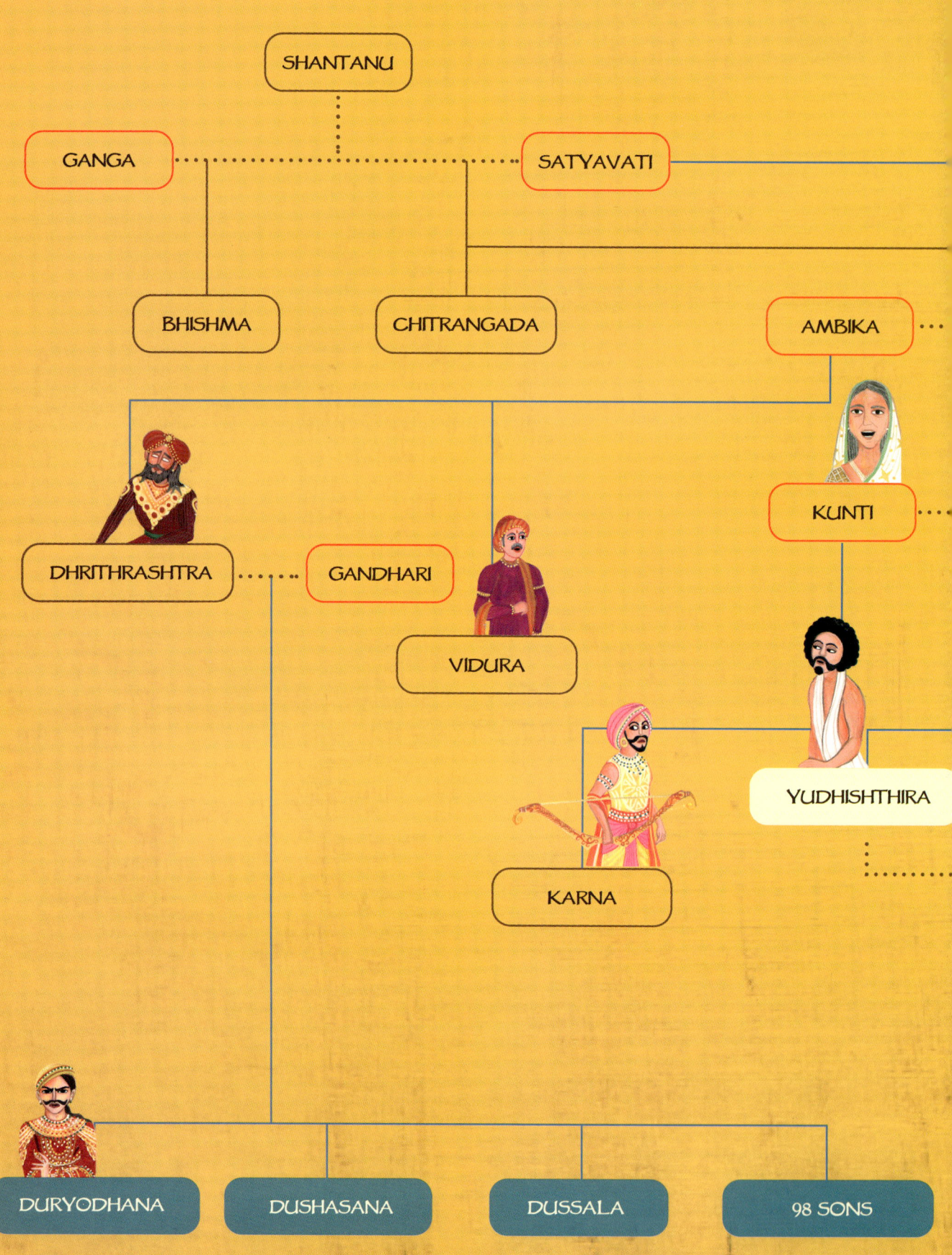

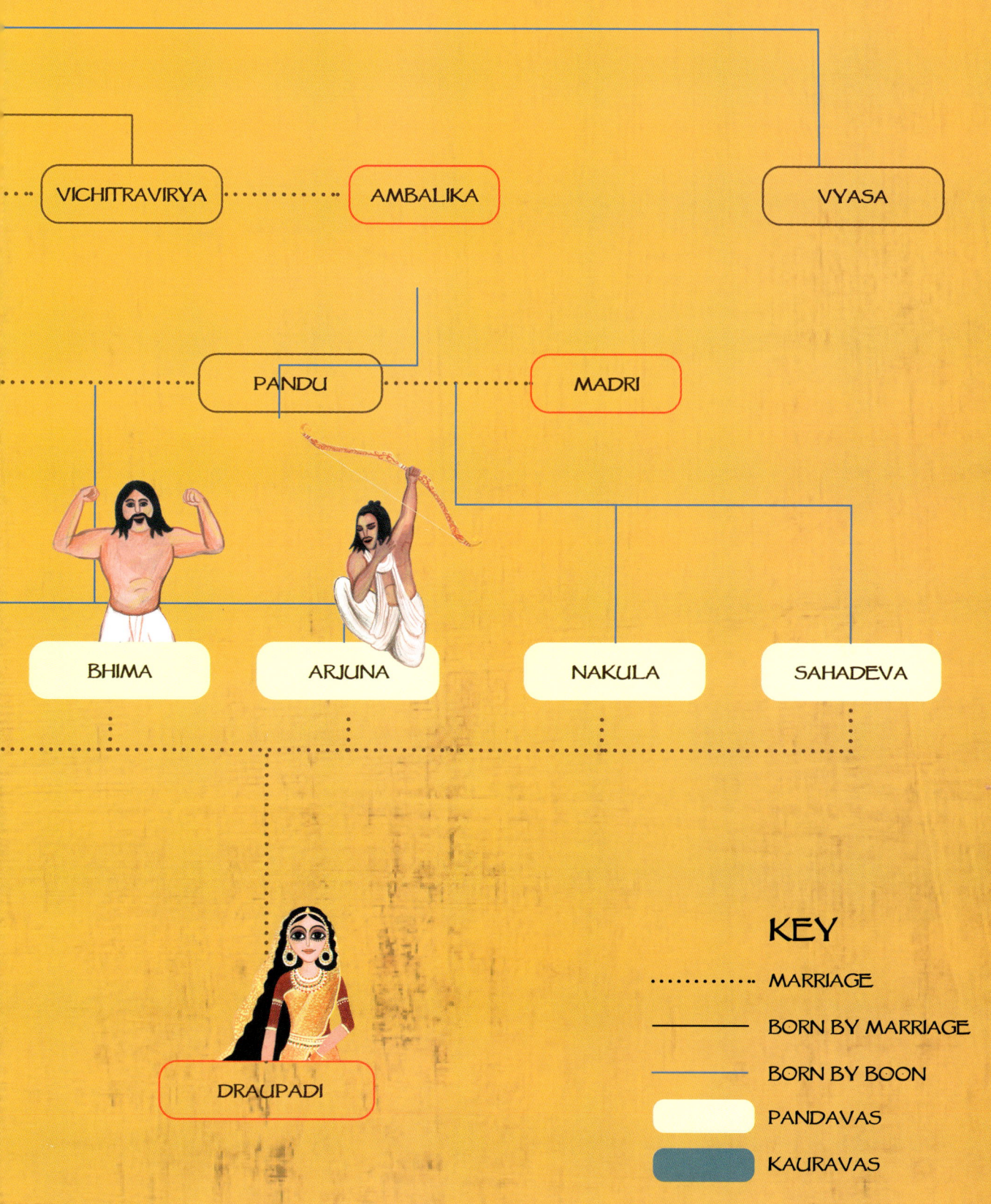

KEY CHARACTERS

DRAUPADI

Draupadi was a young and beautiful girl, born from the flames of a fire yagna to King Drupada of Panchala, along with her brother Dhrishtadyumna. When Drapaudi grew up, Arjuna won her swayamvar and eventually she married all the five Pandavas.

KARNA

Karna was born to young Kunti by the boon of Lord Surya. He was raised by a charioteer Adhiratha and his wife Radha. Later, he became, a supremely skilled archer known for his loyalty and friendship with Duryodhana.

ARJUNA

Arjuna was the third of the Pandava brothers born to Kunti by the boon of Lord Indra. He was the greatest archer in the country. Arjuna was Dronacharya's favourite pupil.

DRUPADA

Drupada was the King of Panchala and the childhood friend of Dronacharya. He performed a great yagna and became the father of Draupadi and Dhristadhyumna who emerged from the fire.

DHRISHTADYUMNA

Dhrishtadyumna was the brave son of King Drupada of Panchala. He was born with his sister Draupadi from a yagna. King Drupada had prayed for his birth to defeat Dronacharya, the guru of the Pandavas.

DURYODHANA

Duryodhana was the eldest brother amongst the Kauravas and born to princess Gandhari as a blessing from sage Vyasa. He was very jealous of the Pandavas.

PANDAVAS IN EKACHARYA

The brave Pandava princes and their mother Kunti had been living in a quiet town called Ekacharya. A friendly Brahmin family had generously given them place to live in their house. Disguised as brahmins, Arjuna and his brothers would go to town every day to earn their living. Upon returning, their mother divided their earnings equally among them.

One night, a man came to the Brahmin's house. In the dim light of the night, he whispered, 'I have something very important to tell you all. King Drupada of Panchala is holding a *swayamvar* for the marriage of his beautiful daughter Draupadi.'

THE BIRTH OF DRAUPADI

King Drupada and Dronacharya were childhood friends. They had learnt archery together. After some years, Drupada became the King of Panchala, while Dronacharya remained poor. One day, Dronacharya went to Panchala to ask King Drupada for help.

King Drupada insulted Dronacharya and asked him to leave. Dronacharya returned to Hastinapur determined to take revenge.

A few years later, Dronacharya instructed the Pandava and Kaurava princes to defeat King Drupada in order to take his revenge.

Arjuna and Bhima defeated King Drupada and brought him captive to Dronacharya. King Drupada's kingdom was also taken over. Dronacharya decided to keep half of Panchala.

This left King Drupada furious. He thought to himself, "I will never forgive Dronacharya for what he has done. I will train my son to kill Dronacharya."

But he was very impressed with Arjuna. "He is the most skilled and the bravest prince I have ever seen! Some day my daughter will marry him."

For years, King Drupada wandered in forests praying for a son to defeat Dronacharya and a daughter to marry Arjuna. One day, he met two sages, Yaja and Upajaya. They heard King Drupada and said, "We will grant your wishes. But for that to happen, you have to serve us for a year." King Drupada agreed to do so.

A year passed and as promised, the sages performed a *yagna*.

From the blazing fire of the *yagna*, emerged Drupada's twin children. A charming young daughter, Draupadi, and a muscular and strong son, Dhrishtadyumna.

King Drupada was overjoyed! He had prayed for this day for years! Both his children were just as Drupada had wished for. Draupadi was also called *Yajnaseni*, born out of *yagna*. Drupada embraced his children and returned to his palace.

The Pandavas had been listening to the man carefully. 'King Drupada is very impressed by Arjuna's skill and strength. He believes that the contest will bring Arjuna to Panchala. And since there is no other prince more skilled than Arjuna, he will win the contest and marry princess Draupadi,' the man said.

The man finished his story. After a while, Arjuna said to the other Pandavas, 'We must go to the *swayamvar* in Panchala!' His brothers agreed.

The next morning, the Pandavas packed their bags, thanked the brahmin family for their kindness and left for Panchala.

THE SPINNING FISH

Panchala was buzzing with excitement. Across the kingdom, people were preparing for the grand event. King Drupada, on the other hand, was anxiously waiting for Arjuna to arrive.

The day of the contest arrived. The people of Panchala had been eagerly waiting to see the suitors compete to marry princess Draupadi.

Princes from all over the country reached Panchala for the grand contest in Drupada's court.

The princes were led to the courtroom to take their seats. The Pandavas entered the court disguised as brahmins so that no one could recognize them.

Princess Draupadi entered, led by her brother Dhrishtadyumna. Dressed in red silk with exquisite golden ornaments, Draupadi looked beautiful. She walked to the end of the court with a garland of flowers in her hands and waited quietly.

Dhrishtadyumna welcomed everybody and said, 'We have gathered for the marriage of my sister princess Draupadi. Here is a bow and five metal arrows. A wheel has been placed at the centre of the court with a wooden fish on it. A tank of water is placed so that the reflection of the fish can be seen. Each suitor has to look down at the reflection and shoot an arrow in the eye of the fish above.'

'Remember you will get only five arrows to try your luck! The winner will be married to princess Draupadi.'

The crowd gasped. This was an impossible task! The kings and princes who had gathered in the court looked at each other. How could they look at a reflection and hit the moving fish above?

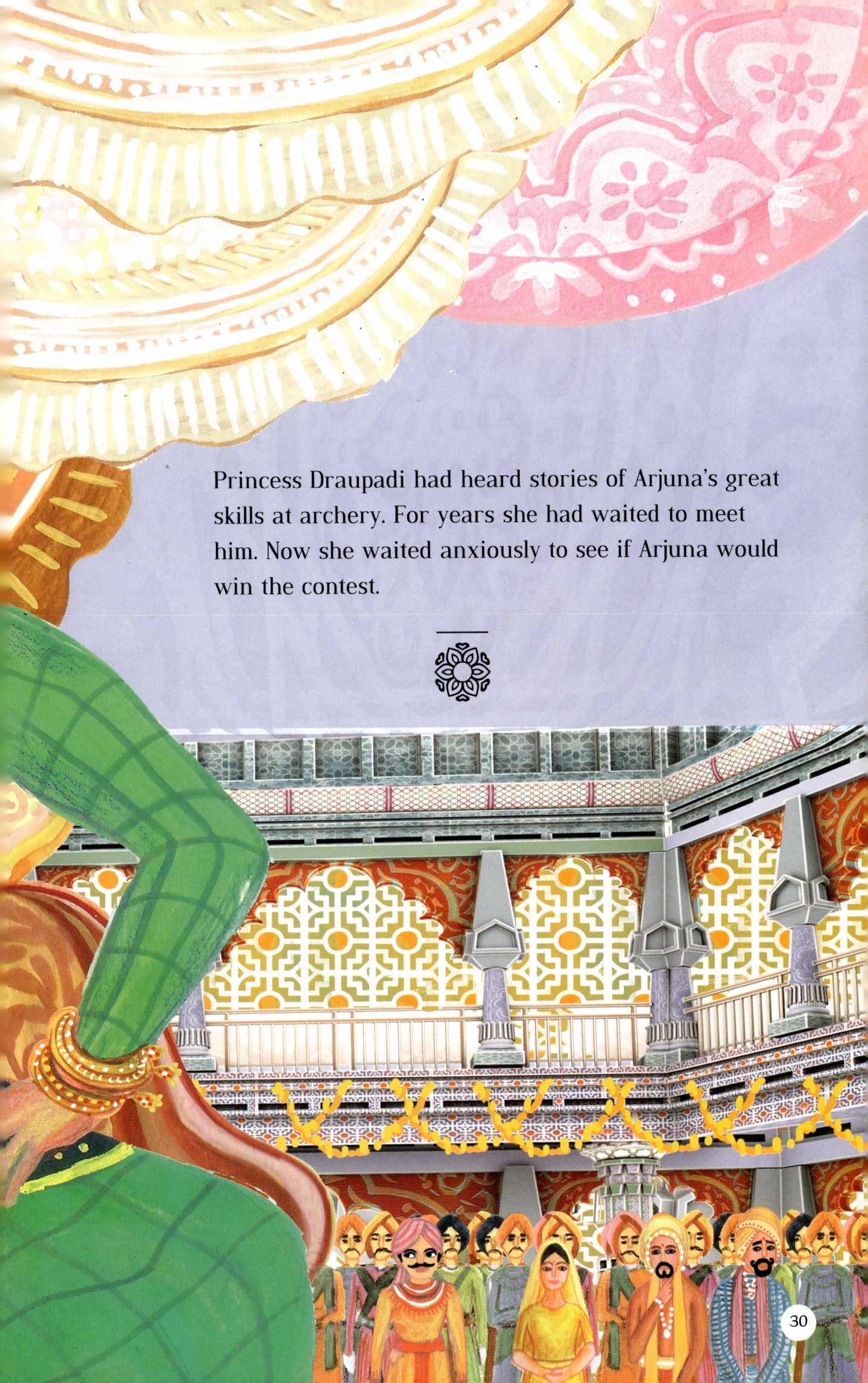

Princess Draupadi had heard stories of Arjuna's great skills at archery. For years she had waited to meet him. Now she waited anxiously to see if Arjuna would win the contest.

THE CONTEST

The competition started. One by one, the princes came forward and tried to aim at the fish's eye. Each of them failed and returned to their seats.

Then entered Duryodhana, eldest of the Kaurava brothers. The crowd looked on attentively. In spite of being cousins, Duryodhana and Arjuna were considered to be the biggest competitors.

One after the other, Duryodhana shot the five arrows but each time he missed the fish's eye. Duryodhana walked back disappointed at losing the contest.

It was now Karna's turn. Karna was Kunti's son but had been raised by a charioteer Adhiratha and his wife Radha. Some years back when Karna had faced Arjuna in an archery competition at Hastinapur, Duryodhana had crowned Karna as the King of Anga.

The Pandavas looked on anxiously as Karna confidently walked up to the dais. Karna raised his arrow and focused on the target above. Just before he could shoot his arrow, a loud voice interrupted him. It was princess Draupadi. She rose from her seat at the end of the court and said, 'Stop right there, Karna! I will not marry a charioteer's son!'

Karna was shocked. He lowered his bow. Without saying a word, he returned to his seat.

Next, Arjuna walked to the arena. Disguised as a brahmin, Arjuna was bright and confident.

He glanced at the fish's eye and the vessel of water. No one recognized Arjuna.

Arjuna aimed straight at the fish's eye. Without blinking, he raised his bow and shot all five arrows right into the eye of the fish! He did not miss the target even once!

The entire arena rose in loud applause. Everyone wanted to know who this great archer was! There was confusion and anger amongst all the kings and princes. Amidst the chaos, Arjuna along with the other Pandavas took Draupadi and ran out of the court.

THE UNUSUAL WEDDING

Drupada saw Draupadi leave the courtroom with Arjuna and Bhima. He was curious to know who this brahmin was. He suspected it was none other than Arjuna. He instructed Dhrishtadyumna to follow them and find out who they really were.

The Pandavas were eager to introduce Draupadi to their mother Kunti and tell her about the contest. On reaching the door of their house, Bhima called out, 'Mother! Come here quickly. See what we got today!'

Every day when her sons returned home, Kunti would tell them to divide their earnings equally amongst themselves.

So when Kunti heard her sons call out for her at the door, she replied, 'Share it equally among yourselves, sons!'

Confused, the Pandavas looked at each other. Since they never disobeyed their mother, they had no choice but to accept their mother's instructions.

All this while, Dhrishtadyumna had been hiding behind the door. He heard everything and realized who the brahmins really were. He ran back to Drupada and said, 'Father, you were right! It was the mighty Arjuna who took Draupadi away!'

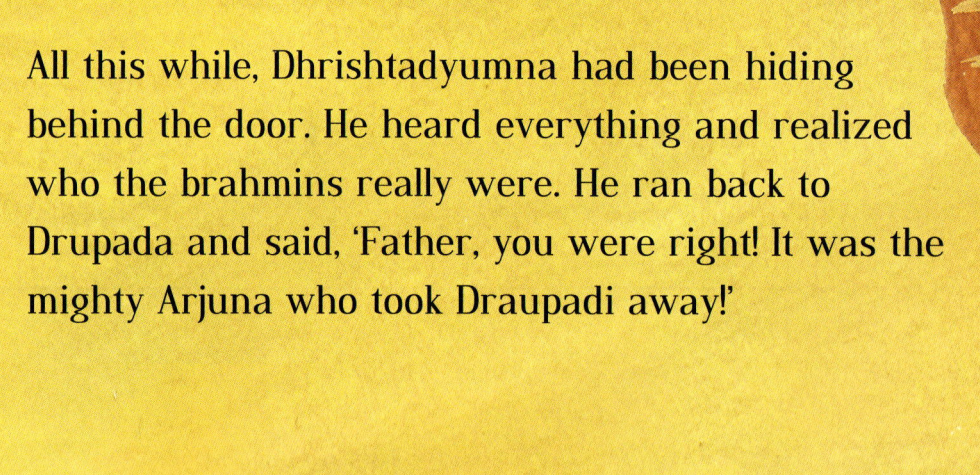

Drupada rose in happiness! He said, 'That's great news, son! Let us invite the Pandavas, Kunti and Draupadi to Panchala for the wedding celebrations!'

So princess Draupadi became the wife of the five Pandavas and all of them lived together happily.

TITLES IN THIS SERIES

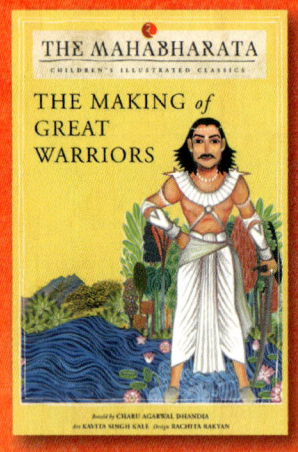
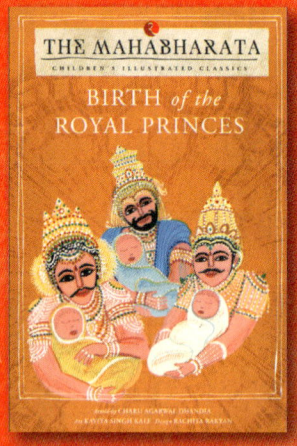
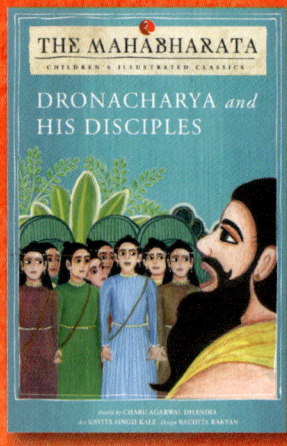
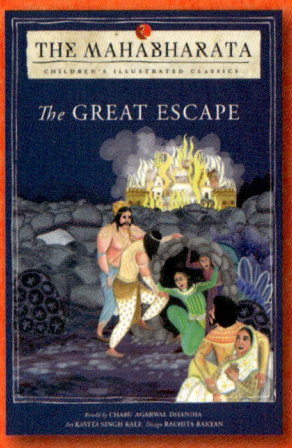
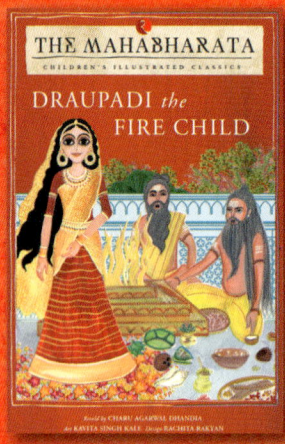
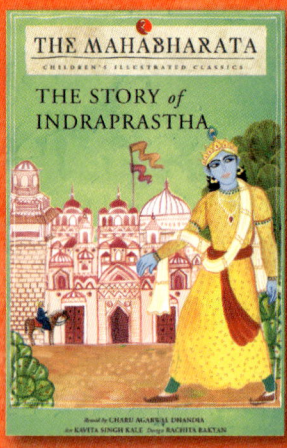
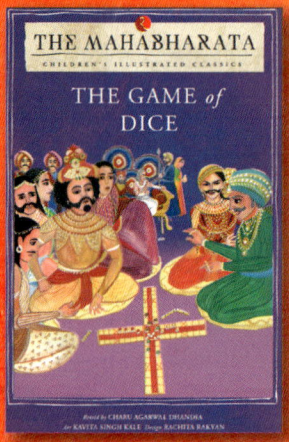
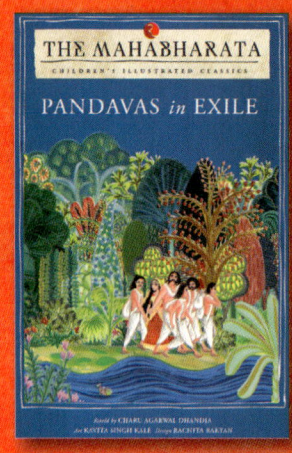
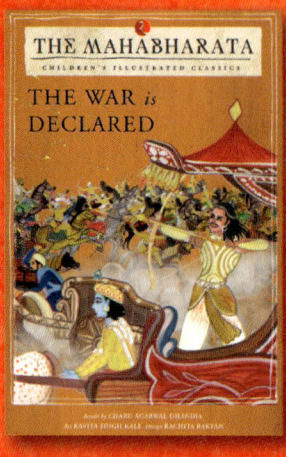